Introduction

The artworks presented here are taken from the archive of *Curtis's Botanical Magazine*, the longest-running periodical featuring colour illustrations of plants in the world. Founded in 1787 by apothecary and botanist William Curtis (1746–99) as *The Botanical Magazine*, it appealed to scientists as well as ladies and gentlemen wanting information on the many newly introduced ornamental flowers that were in vogue in the gardens of the wealthy and fashionable. The 19th century saw a proliferation of plant collecting, with new species being sought out to satisfy the Victorian craze for the unusual and exotic.

Each issue of the magazine contained three hand-coloured copper-engraved plates alongside the text which described the Linnaean name, genus and qualities, along with botanical, horticultural and historical background, associated information relating to what we might now call conservation, and any economic applications or uses. Curtis charged one shilling per month and soon had 2,000 subscribers. Accomplished artists were commissioned to produce the plates, and the magazine was an instant success. The plates continued to be hand-coloured until 1948, when a scarcity of colourists led to the implementation of photographic reproduction.

The name of the magazine was changed to *Curtis's Botanical Magazine* after Curtis's death in 1799. It was first produced at Kew in 1841, when William Jackson Hooker (1785–1865) moved south from Glasgow University to become Director of the Royal Botanic Gardens. Joseph Dalton Hooker (1817–1911) took over the role of editor from his father in 1865, and the magazine has continued to be produced by Kew Gardens' staff and artists to this day.

All but one of the artworks included here are by Walter Hood Fitch (1817–92), who illustrated more than 2,700 plants for the magazine and published over 10,000 illustrations during his career. Plate 43 is by his student, Harriet Thiselton-Dyer (1854–1945), who was Joseph Hooker's daughter. Her contribution of around 100 illustrations between 1878 and 1880 helped keep the magazine in publication after Fitch's sudden resignation in 1877.

Presented in this compilation are 44 colour plates of exotic plants together with their corresponding black and white lithographs for you to try your hand at colouring. The original watercolour drawings were made from life, so you can be sure that your finished renderings are based on accurate and precise representations of the actual plants. A key to the plates, using plant names given at the time of publication, can be found in the next few pages. The current names of these plants can usually be found on the Internet, and you may even discover a reference to the original plate.

Key: List of plates

1 *Gardenia malleifera*

2 *Mamillaria clava*

3 *Echinocactus chlorophthalmus*

4 *Sida integerrima*

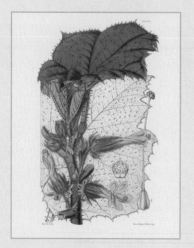

5 *Hibiscus ferox*

6. *Passiflora amabilis*

7 *Curcuma cordata*

8 *Alloplectus capitatus*

9 *Echinocactus rhodophthalmus*

10 *Nymphaea ampla*

11 *Begonia thwaitesii*

12 *Tacsonia sanguinea*

The Kew Gardens
EXOTIC PLANTS
COLOURING BOOK

*Over 40 beautiful illustrations
plus colour guides*

ARCTURUS

ROYAL BOTANIC GARDENS

All illustrations included in this book have been taken from the Library,
Art & Archives Collections of the Royal Botanic Gardens, Kew.

Special thanks to Lynn Parker, Art and Illustrations Curator, and
Dr Martyn Rix, Editor of *Curtis's Botanical Magazine*.

ARCTURUS

This edition published in 2017 by Arcturus Publishing Limited
26/27 Bickels Yard, 151–153 Bermondsey Street,
London SE1 3HA

ISBN: 978-1-78404-565-4
CH004520NT
Supplier 29, Date 0717, Print Run 6316

Printed in China

13 *Hibiscus radiatus*

14 *Crinum giganteum*

15 *Haemanthus insignis*

16 *Ananas bracteatus*

17 *Nepenthes villosa*

18 *Cattleya granulosa*

19 *Fuchsia simplicicaulis*

20 *Caladium bicolor*

21 *Lindenia rivalis*

22 *Portlandia platantha*

23 *Mutisia decurrens*

24 *Vriesea xiphostachys*

25 *Limatodes rosea*

26 *Ipomoea alatipes*

27 *Agave glaucescens*

28 *Cypripedium hookerae*

29 *Encephalartos horridus*

30 *Alstromeria caldasii*

31 *Aechmea distichantha*

32 *Dendrobrium farmeri*

33 *Habranthus fulgens*

34 *Morenia fragrans*

35 *Urceolina pendula*

36 *Phalaenopsis schilleriana*

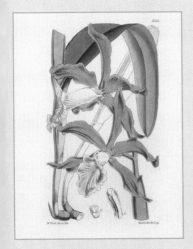

37 *Laelia grandis*

38 *Dipteracanthus affinis*

39 *Dendrobrium dixanthum*

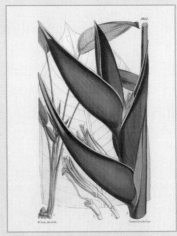

40 *Heliconia humilis*

41 *Cattleya dowiana*

42 *Eranthemum cinnabarinum*

43 *Rondeletia odorata*

44 *Citrus aurantium*

4307

Fitch del. & lith.

4307

Fitch del. & lith.

Fitch, del et lith.

Reeve, Benham & Reeve, imp.

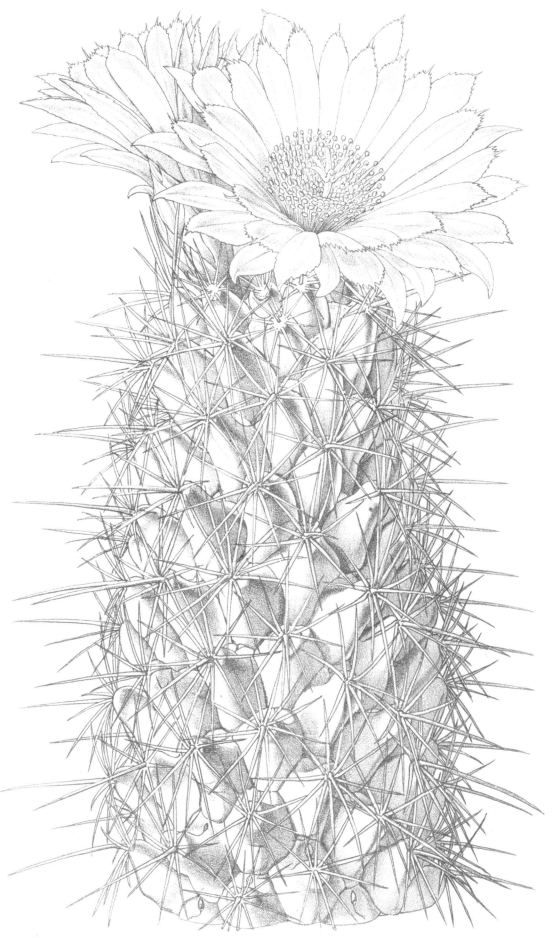

4358.

4373.

Fitch del et lith.

Reeve, Benham & Reeve, imp.

4373.

Fitch del et lith.   Reeve, Benham & Reeve, imp.

Reeve, Benham & Reeve, imp.

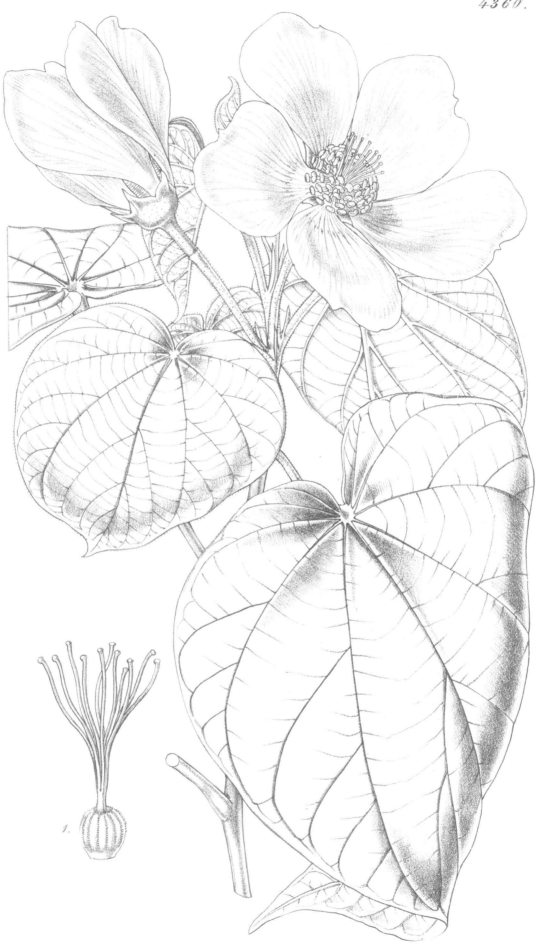

4360.

Reeve, Benham & Reeve, imp.

Fitch, del. et lith.

Reeve, Benham & Reeve imp.

Fitch del. et lith.

Reeve, Benham & Reeve imp.

Fitch, del. et lith.

R, B & R, imp.

4406.

Fitch del et lith.

R, B & R, imp.

4435.

Fitch, del. et lith.

R. B. & R. imp.

Fitch, del. et lith.

R. B. & R. imp.

Fitch. del et lith.

R. B. & R. imp

Fitch del et lith.

R. B. & R. imp.

Fitch del et lith.

R.B. & R. imp.

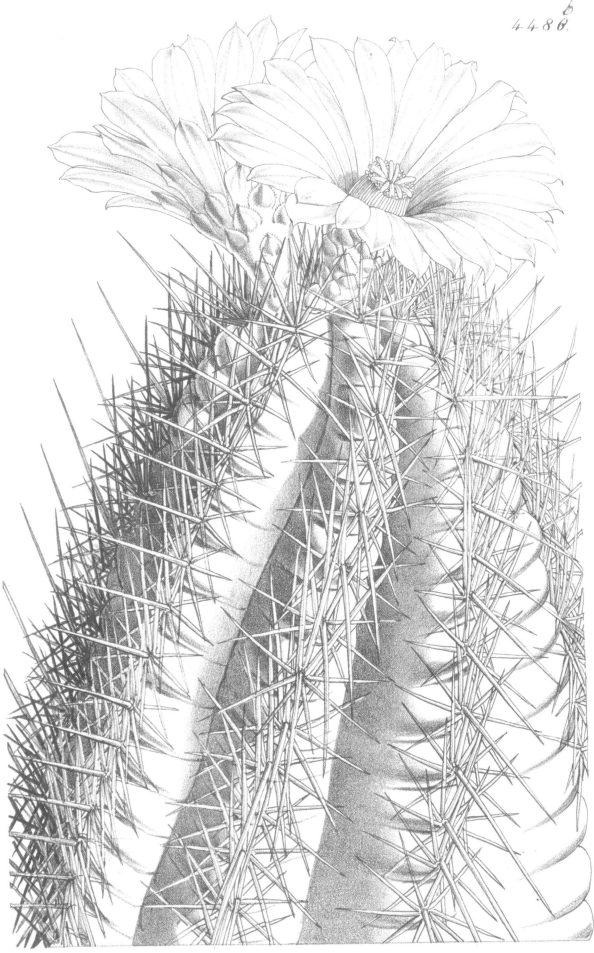

Fitch del et lith.

R.B. & R. imp.

4469.

Fitch del et lith.

R. B. & R. imp.

Fitch del et lith.

R. B. & R. imp.

4692.

Fitch, del et lith.

1.

F. Reeve, imp

4692.

Fitch, del et lith.

F. Reeve, imp

Fitch, del et lith.

F. Reeve, imp.

Fitch, del et lith.

F. Reeve, imp.

W.Fitch, del. et lith.

Vincent Brooks, Imp.

W.Fitch, del. et lith.

Vincent Brooks, Imp.

5205.

W.Fitch,del.et lith.

Vincent Brooks, Imp.

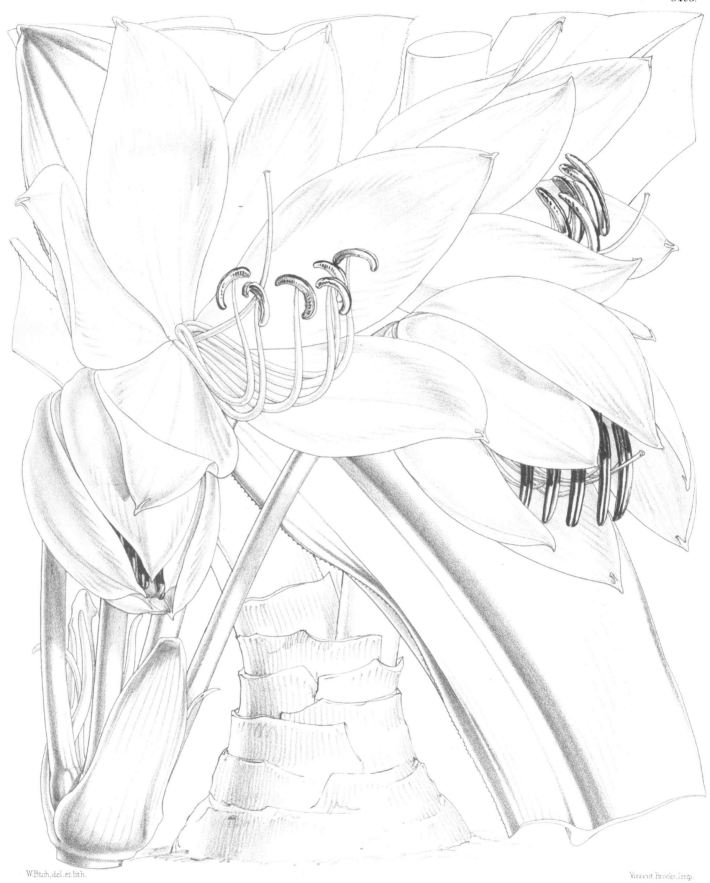

W.Fitch,del.et lith.

Vincent Brooks,Imp.

4745.

Fitch, del. et lith.

F. Reeve, imp.

Fitch, del. et lith.

F Reeve, imp.

5025.

W. Fitch del. et lith.

Vincent Brooks Imp.

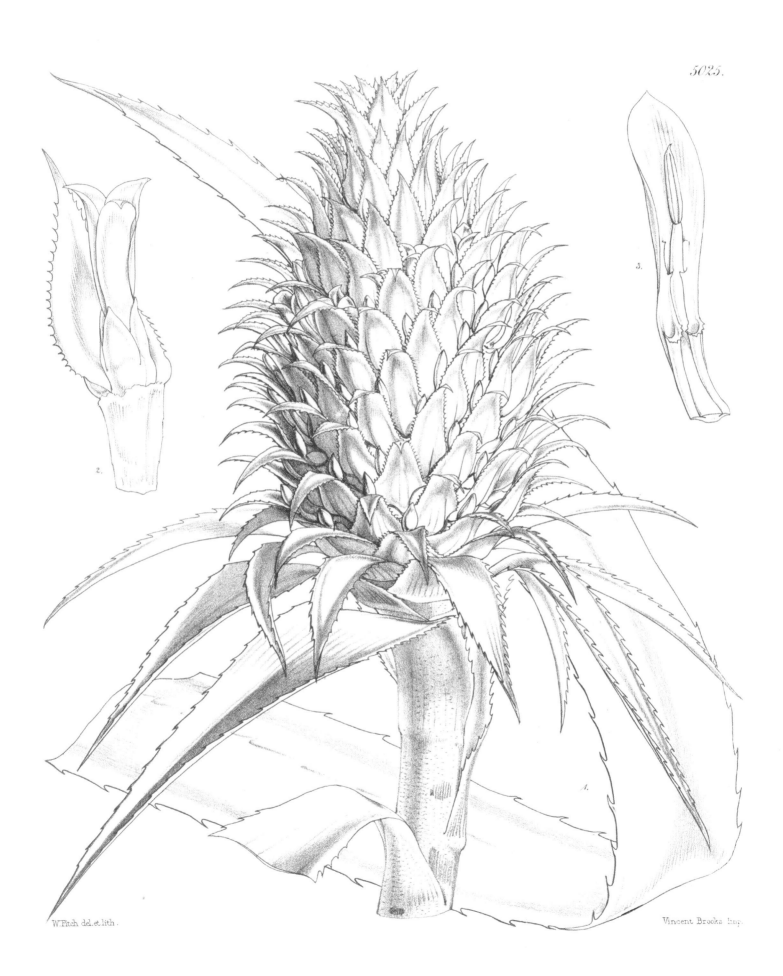

5025.

5080.

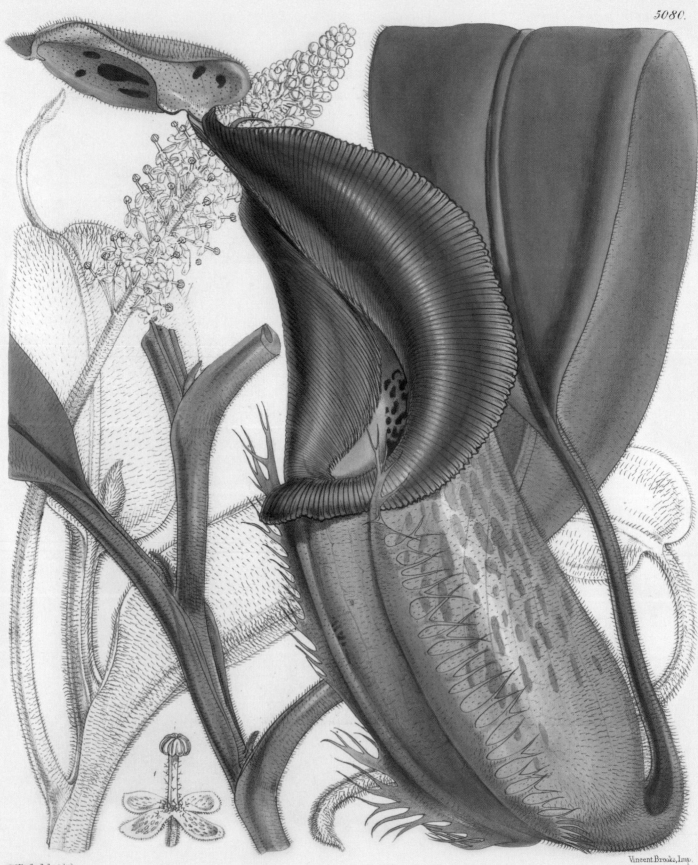

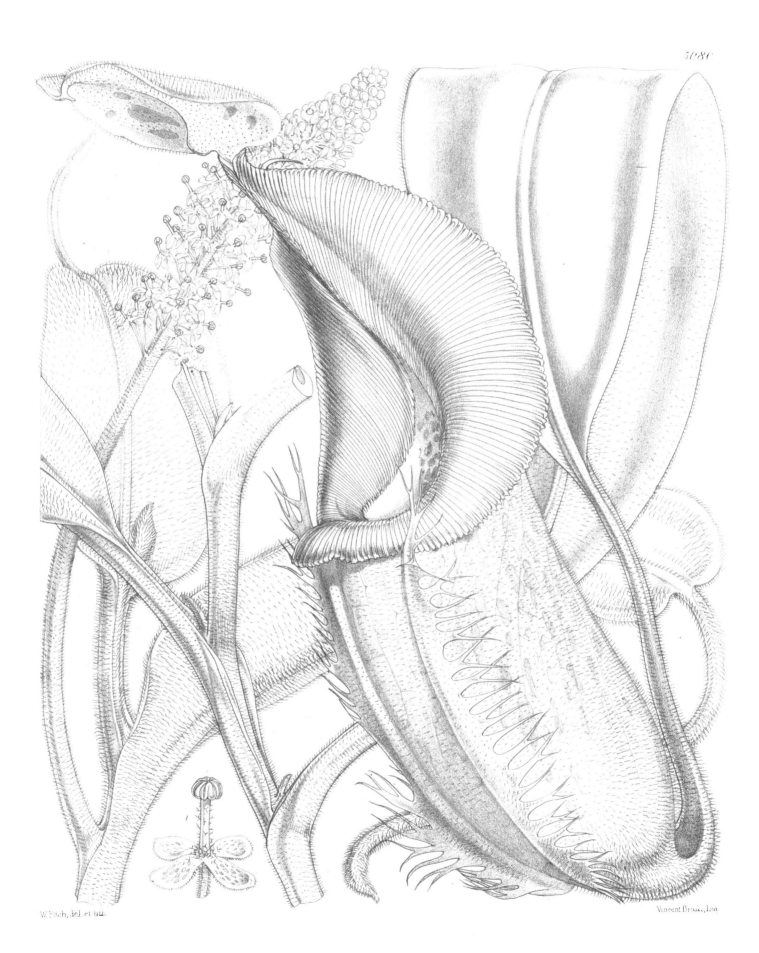

5080

1.

5096.

W. Fitch, delt et lith.

Vincent Brooks, Imp.

W. Fitch, delt et lith.

Vincent Brooks, Imp.

5255.

W. Fitch, del. et lith.

Vincent Brooks, Imp.

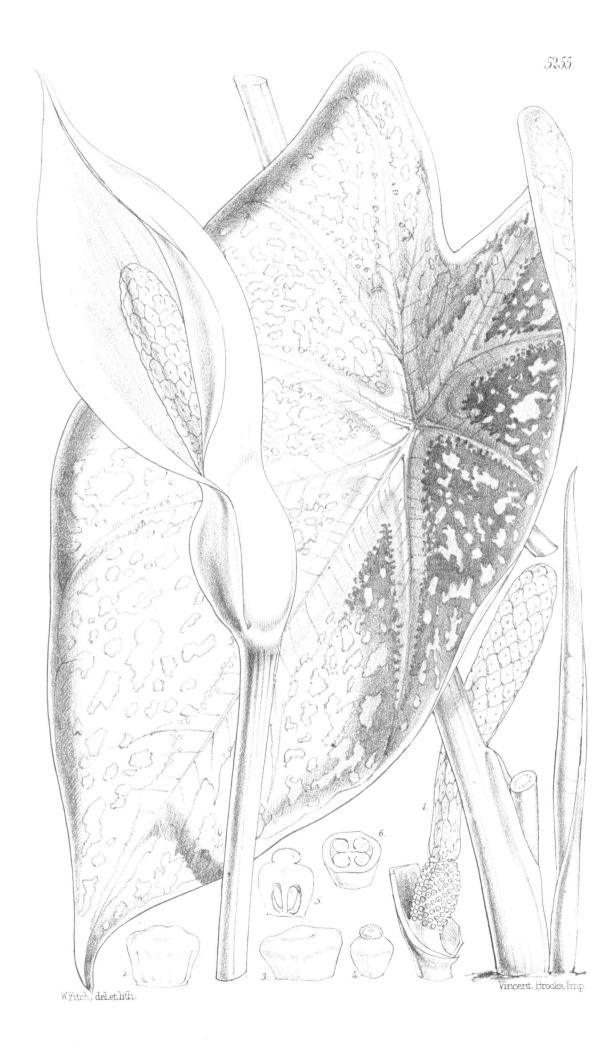

W. Fitch, del. et lith.

Vincent Brooks, Imp.

5258.

W. Fitch, del. et lith.

Vincent Brooks, Imp.

W Fitch, del. et lith.

Vincent Brooks, Imp.

Fitch del et lith.

F. Reeve, imp.

Fitch del et lith.

F. Reeve, imp.

5273

W.Fitch, del et lith.

Vincent Brooks, Imp.

5287.

W. Fitch, del. et lith.

Vincent Brooks, Imp.

5287.

W. Fitch, del. et lith.

Vincent Brooks, Imp.

5312.

W. Fitch, del. et lith.

Vincent Brooks, Imp.

1.

W.Fitch, del et lith.

Vincent Brooks, Imp.

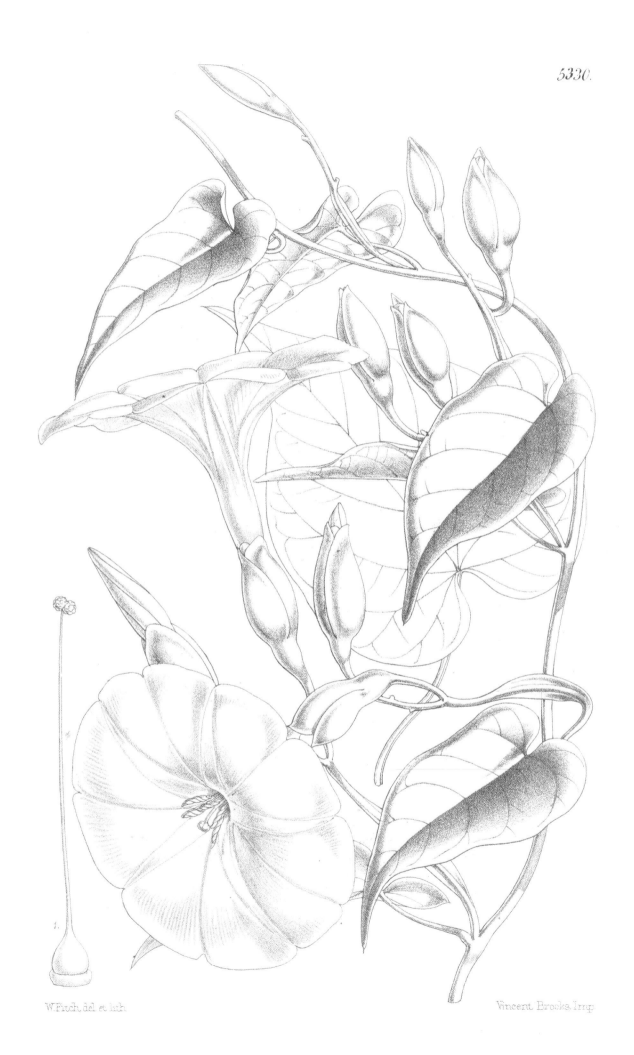

5330.

5033.

W. Fitch, del et lith.

Vincent Brooks, Imp.

W Fitch.del et lith.

Vincent Brooks, Imp.

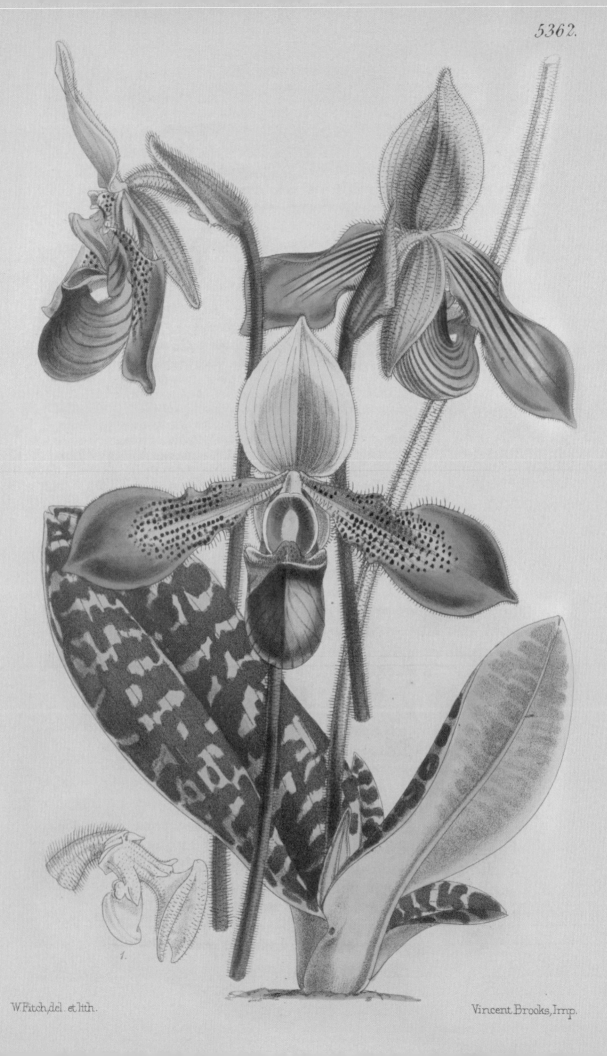

W. Fitch, del. et lith.

1.

Vincent Brooks, Imp.

5371.

W. Fitch, del. et lith.

Vincent Brooks, Imp.

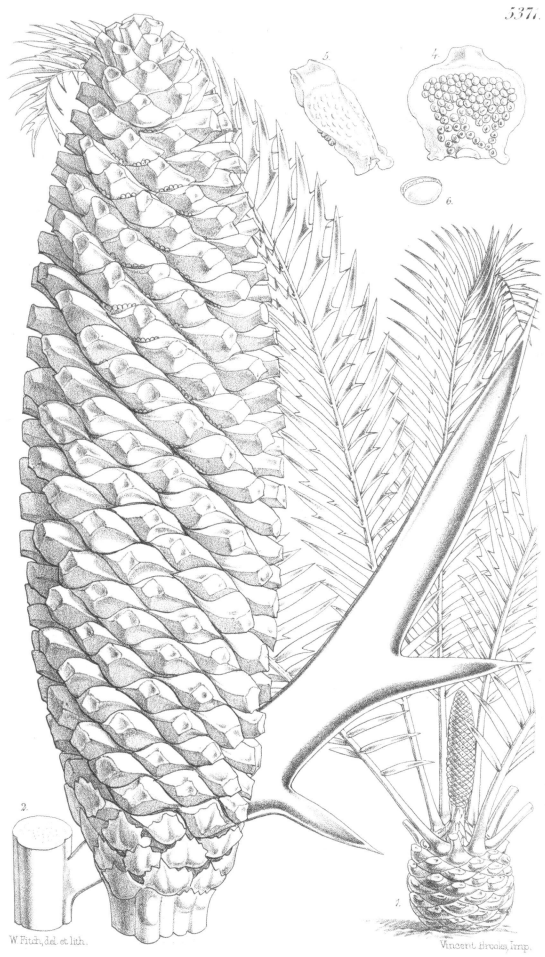

W. Fitch del. et lith.

Vincent Brooks Imp.

W.Fitch, del et lith.

Vincent Brooks, Imp.

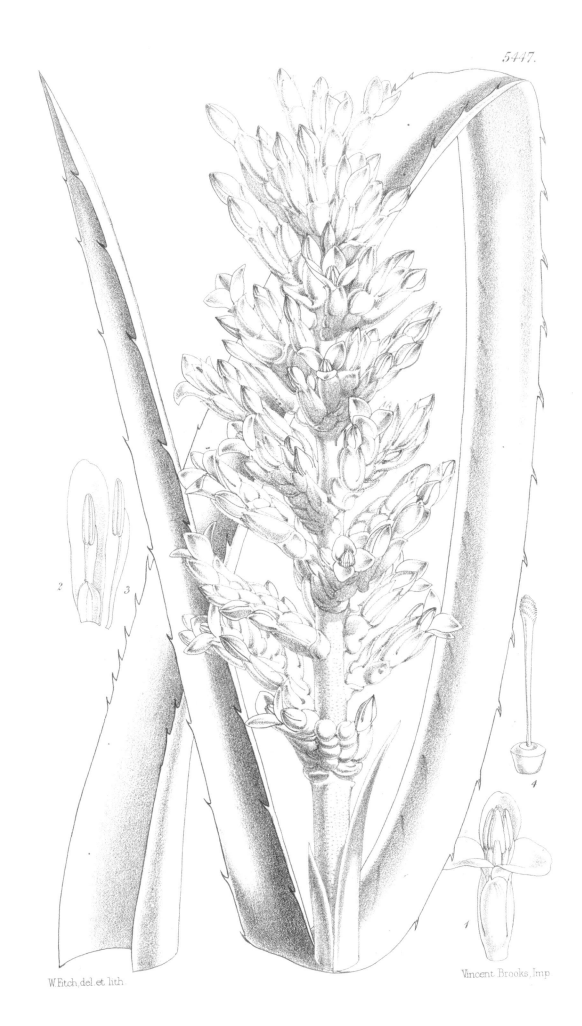

5447.

W. Fitch, del. et lith.

Vincent Brooks, Imp.

5451.

W. Fitch, del et lith.

Vincent Brooks, Imp.

W. Fitch, del et lith.

Vincent Brooks, Imp.

5563.

W.Fitch,del.et lith.

Vincent Brooks,Imp.

5492.

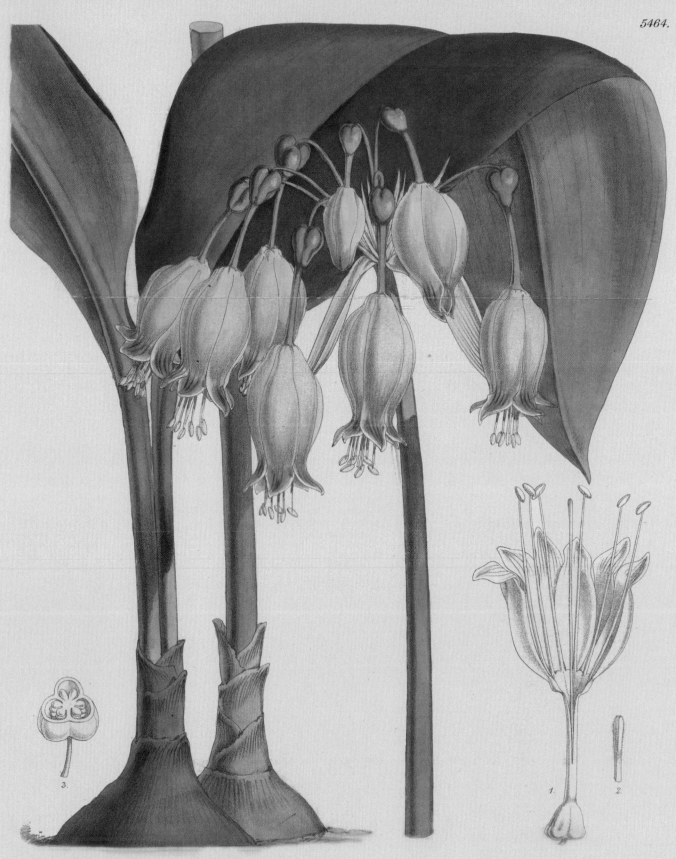

5464.

W. Fitch, del. et lith.

Vincent Brooks, Imp.

W.Fitch,del et lith.

Vincent Brooks, Imp.

5530.

W. Fitch, del. et lith.

Vincent. Brooks, Imp.

W. Fitch, del. et lith.

Vincent Brooks, Imp.

5553.

W. Fitch, del. et lith.

Vincent Brooks, Imp.

5414.

W. Fitch, del. et lith.

Vincent Brooks, Imp.

5414.

1.

W.Fitch, del. et lith.

Vincent Brooks, Imp.

5564.

W. Fitch, del. et lith.

Vincent Brooks, Imp.

2.

1.

5564.

5613.

W. Fitch, del. et lith.

Vincent Brooks, Imp.

W. Fitch, del. et lith.

Vincent Brooks, Imp

5618.

W. Fitch, del. et lith.

Vincent Brooks, Imp.

5618.

W. Fitch, del et lith.

Vincent Brooks, Imp.

5921.

1.

2.

W. Fitch. del. et lith.

Vincent Brooks, Day & Son, Imp.

1.

2.

W. Fitch. del. et lith.

Vincent Brooks, Day & Son, Imp.

6350

H.T.D. del. J N Fitch Lith.

Vincent Brooks Day & Son Imp

L. Reeve & Cº London

6350

H.T.D. del J N Fitch Lith   Vincent Brooks Day &Son Imp

L.Reeve &C° London

6128

1

2

W.Fitch, del et lith.

Vincent Brooks Day & Son, Imp

1

2